WIPE YOUR FACE,

YOU JUST SWALLOWED MY SOUL

OTHER BOOKS BY HUGH PRATHER

I Touch the Earth, the Earth Touches Me

Notes to Myself

HUGH PRATHER

Wipe Your Face, You Just Swallowed My Soul

DOUBLEDAY & COMPANY, INC.
GARDEN CITY, NEW YORK
1974

The cover drawing and the illustrations are all reproductions of the original paintings and drawings of John Philip Wagner. Mr. Wagner exhibits in Santa Fe, New Mexico, his home, and in other cities.

The illustrations on pages 34, 50, 66, and 70 are details. None of the art in this book may be reproduced without written permission from the publisher.

ISBN: 0-385-06207-9 Trade
0-385-06211-7 Paperbound
Library of Congress Catalog Card Number: 74-11642
Copyright © 1974 by Hugh Prather
All Rights Reserved
Printed in the United States of America
First Edition

"This lady is going to have a baby, Nick," he said.

"I know," said Nick.

"You don't know," said his father. *"Listen to me. What she is going through is called being in labor. The baby wants to be born and she wants it to be born. All her muscles are trying to get the baby born. That is what is happening when she screams."*

From "Indian Camp" by Ernest Hemingway

5:23

We start out at twilight, that interval before drug-store robberies and felonious assaults, when the mind labors to pass the ostium of a wasted day, but like an exit in a house of mirrors it will not be passed.

A mauve hatchet hangs in the sky where the sun has been, and as we move out we can hear the pule of a loon.

5:46

Because the light is poor we are stumbling into these rubbery gray forms which grow from the earth. I hear curses and whines from other members of the group as they encounter them. The plants, if indeed they are plants, stud the ground in no discernible pattern and have a movement not altogether account-able from the shifts in the wind. They are warm to the touch as though they were sucking the dead day's heat from the earth, and each time I force my way over one I feel chilled from the contact.

6:05

It is difficult for me to make out how many are in the expedition. There is a woman near me. She seems determined to walk either before or after me, never by my side. Her face has those long flat lines which symbolize intelligence and a nose that in the failing light occasionally appears to turn up. She is wearing a man's short-sleeve white shirt like the heroine in some 1940s movie. I cannot tell how small her breasts are but I am certain they are not massive.

There is someone behind me who from time to time composes a poem to the hatchet, which has now cleaved the horizon and is spraying a clotted red over this treacherous ground cover, but I cannot detect any effect from this ritual on either the hatchet or the plants.

Something large is moving to our right.

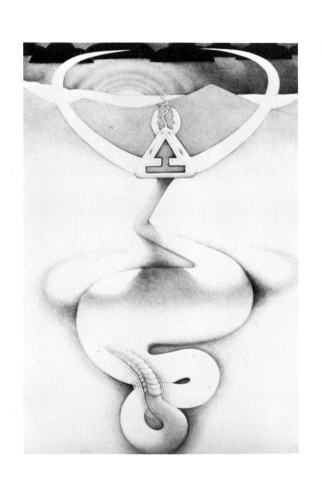

6:27
___

The hatchet has sunk below the horizon, followed by a black sky that could have been the hand which wielded it.

Now we feel the moon trying to come up, something wanting to leave a stomach.

6:52

We have finally made it through the hole where the moon had risen like a bubble in putrid lard. But I can't talk about it . . . except to say this: I now know all too well who is in this expedition.

7:13

The person behind me now recites only one poem, his voice like a dying man's confession. I have told him repeatedly to shut up (at which moments the white-shirted woman always brushes past me in a pet) but his concentration is so absolute that he apparently doesn't hear.

It is evident that the plants are undergoing a subtle transmutation. At first I thought this was a trick of the thick lunar light but I have just noticed that I no longer hear curses from the other members. The plants now appear to sway forward as I connect with them and even seem to paw lightly down my thigh as I walk away, although I cannot bring myself to believe that the latter is a type of primitive volition. Still, the parting stroke is so gentle and well placed that I am left in a state of confusion every time I leave one.

The woman (now in front of me) has just asked if the plants seem to spring upward as I disengage them. I will not answer.

7:33

The movement to our right, which I thought before was monolithic, has turned out to be bats. They crossed over us a few moments ago, a soundless spasm. A thick-ankled young man wearing glasses came back and told us that they are a type of South American bat which sucks blood. He seemed quite pleased that they suck blood. A curious thing happened when he was here. A boy of about five and a girl of I would guess thirteen walked hand in hand out of the dark. Although the night is still warm I was nevertheless startled that they were unclothed. They walked quietly over to us, listened to the dissertation on bats, then walked back into the same point in the darkness. They were remarkable for their soft untouched beauty. The boy had a large rosy head and enormous blue eyes. His limbs were plump like a baby's. The skin and hair of the girl were a deep blond as though her body had been dipped totally in a vat of gold. Her almond eyes seemed almost to explode in long buttered lashes.

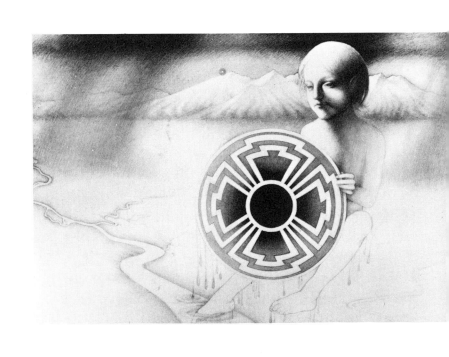

7:53

I am surprised that I am feeling no anxiety for the children's safety. But as a pair they were so serenely autonomous that they appeared in need of protection from no one. I find myself at once filled with their lovely image, and the memory of the bats. They writhed over us, rooting the air like rabid pigs, then for a moment stilling their succussion as if they had suddenly detected a nest of moles, blind and somnolent.

The children walked back to our left, which is the identical direction taken by the bats. Evidently that is appropriate.

8:12

Either the bats are choosing to fly over those areas where the plants are stunted, or the plants themselves are shrinking into the ground below their flight (I will assume the former until I obtain definite proof; it is reasonable that their movement is a sway and not a snaking downward). The white-shirted woman announced to no one apparent that she was feeling a tinge of sadness at their departure. She was somehow comforted by rubbing through their appendages. Cow stroking cow.

8:32

The ground seems brighter now, especially bright where the base of a plant still nudges from the soil. I had not given my attention to the ground before. It is pliant and reverberates slightly when struck with a heel or forehead. Its tensility is supple and uniform like the skin of a plum. Evidently it consoles the white-shirted woman for the loss of her plants—we left her behind some moments ago lifting and dropping herself from a squatting posture.

8:52

People ahead of me are running . . .

I hear a shriek.

That must be what is attracting them. But whether it was a shriek of pain or hilarity I couldn't tell.

There it is again. I'm still not close enough to tell. It must be coming from where those people are standing.

This man will not get out of my way.

I may have to fight him in order to see.

It's the young girl. A large bat is stuck to her groin. I'm unable to decide if she is attempting to pull it from her or press it deeper. The others must not know either, for no one is trying to help her. The little boy walks excitedly around as if he were refereeing a contest at a county fair.

Now the others are starting to leave.

I feel impelled to tell them it is not over.

21

9:11

A strange and delicate filament has appeared on the ground, a suspension of hair on a fetus fontanel or the first day's pubescence of a witch. Moonlight is gathering on the strands, purling up each thread, mutating our landscape into something resembling a soft and ciliated star. Those of us who still have shoes on remove them, and as our feet stroke the turf, the strands flowing between our toes like sable, a static electricity begins to move up our legs; flutters into the creases; crawls over our chests, nipping; paws under each joint and knuckle until we have all become laughing boneless bubbles springing over the earth jumping knee first into the rubbery undersurface waving and shouting tearful greetings to each other, and, with our necks careened back, baiting the bobbing cloud of bats.

9:31

As unexpectedly as it came the filament vanished, leaving the ground bald and supple like polished bread. We are again strangers. The terrain was so absorbing that no one recalls what was said; the tears of pleasure so blinded our features that if we now see someone we had spoken to we do not remember.

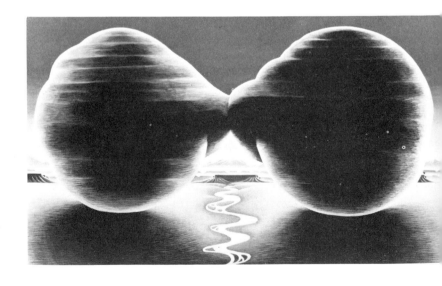

9:43

Something is moving behind me. I believe it is the white-shirted woman.

Yes, it's the woman. And the girl is with her. They are talking. I catch only words and phrases.

How was it?
The bat or the people watching?
The bat.
It was different.
I take it was your first.
Bat?
Yes.
Yes.
Well, how was it?
I've already answered that.
I mean how did it *feel*?
Different.
Different compared to what?
Him.
But he's only six.
Yes I know.
But he couldn't.
Yes I know.

27

9:56

I see a group of men in front of me. I think one
of them is the man I had to fight.

10:08

It seems the men had the little boy and were teasing him about Olah (Olah must be his friend, the girl). At first he appeared not to hear their words, then in an instant he was crying. That either satisfied or disgusted the men and they left. I stopped to see what I could offer. I tried pulling a plant root out of the ground and biting on it and whimpering as if it were in pain, but that only made him cry louder. Then I molded a face in the ground, a large sickle-shaped smile and bulbous nose, and I opened the lips of the smile and put him in. That worked. He started flipping the bottom lip against his knee and forgot all about crying. There was no further need for me to stay.

10:20

For several minutes now the white-shirted woman has been walking in front of me, stooping and picking something off the ground. It is a shiny object, smooth and circular like a planchet. I have evidently been walking over them all the while and didn't know it. She takes each one into her mouth, bites it, then returns it to the same indentation in the ground from which it came. I pick one of these up and see a red ooze coming from the teeth marks. I drop it and wipe my hand between my legs, turning so she will not see. I continue following for several minutes. Suddenly I realize what she is doing and I wheel around. Behind me is a moldering stripe of bats feeding on the disks. One of them is by my heel and I boot it into the air. It lands, decomposed, some twenty feet from me and instantly becomes another supper. I turn away with disgust and walk until I have put the white-shirted woman behind me.

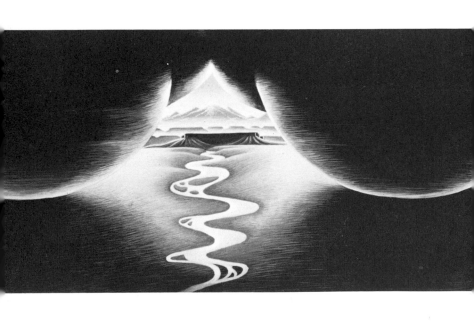

10:26

The terrain is becoming biased, but the downward slant is easy enough to negotiate because the ground wrinkles slightly as a foot pushes into it, thereby forming a transitory step. In the distance the moon is melting and I can see a membranous glow below its dissolution. The light of the glow contains more orange than the light of the moon. Because of our increased pace and the direction taken by the terrain I would guess that it is toward the glow we are headed. The bats flew that way some twenty minutes ago.

10:33

The members of the expedition have developed a consuming thirst. A committee made up of the boy and headed by the young man with glasses has scouted below and located a small patch of plants. One of them had the presence of mind to cut off the tips and discovered inside a perfectly clear liquid, weightless and odorless, which they have reported is excellent for drinking. Something is peculiar about their features, however, and the members fear that this is a consequence of the liquid. Since we will perish if we do not drink soon, and as no one will assure us of when we shall have water, the members are inclined to follow their example (a course that seems well considered under these conditions).

10:39

The effect of the liquid became evident within sec-
onds after we drank. It appears that the external features of the soma drop in perfect correlation with the
unit of liquid consumed. Fortunately, this effect was
duly noted before I began drinking, and as a result I
suffered only a slight elongation in the chest. The effect
on the boy, however, who drank twice, has been quite
striking. Large rolls of his flesh now drag the ground
(due, I am sure, to his smaller stature). The smooth
texture of the soil prevents this from being discomfort-
ing, and the only consequence that seems to annoy
him is the multilinear trail he leaves behind. Even this
is now being eradicated by Olah, who walks in back
of him stamping out the furrows with her bare feet.
She has endeared herself to all of us.

10:45

The young man with glasses has just asked me why Olah has been carrying a cane ever since she drank. I consider the question uncalled for and will not return it.

10:51
___

Now the moon is one third melted, a runoff spilling from the fourth quadrant. The ichor shapes a translucent tube between solar houses, a transfusion under the skin. I cannot help but wonder what the bats see in it.

10:57

The dark encloses, tunnels down our throats. From the others a soundless howl. Funny what brings you together. We circle a giant plant arm screwing from the ground. It gives off heat that is badly needed. The white-shirted woman climbs its tip and rides there like Bellerophon. Others don't find her amusing.

11:00

Other plants are coming out of the ground now that the bats have gone, and I begin searching among the members for the boy. Someone is hiding behind the white-shirted woman, but every time I move in a direction that would allow me to see who it is, the figure counters my move and remains hidden. I walk up to the woman and crush the glasses behind her feet.

I now approach the man I had to fight. Instantly he assumes the horse stance, but I wave my hand indicating this is not necessary. He smiles broadly and embraces me. For several minutes he talks warmly about the expedition. I learn he is not an intelligent man.

11:04

Enough plants have risen so that the heat being lost from the moon is now replaced, and again we start toward the glow. I realize with a certain panic that I haven't taken advantage of the pause to meet new members. There was an old woman pissing on the ground who intrigued me. Her nose was like a pomegranate. Her mouth gave nothing away. I console myself with excuses.

11:07
___

The man I had to fight is running down to the failing moon, kicking over the smaller plants, mounting and snapping with his weight the larger ones, forcing his fingers deep into others and wrenching them bodily from the ground. Although he has succeeded in rupturing large numbers of plants, many more have risen than he could reasonably expect to bring down, yet systematic maiming does not appear to be his goal since he does not proceed in a straight line.

11:09

Some of the ruptured plants split along the line where their base joined the ground and from these openings a stream of small pallid spheres is now beginning to trickle over the ground like a hemorrhage of eggs from a wounded reptile. After our experience with the liquid, no one has wanted to pick one of these up; but the old woman, who joined us late, is cracking them open and passing around the halves. I notice that the interior of the cells reflects an angled glare on the face of the one who holds it, and as he looks inside he immediately and violently throws back his head. This is sufficient reason for me to decline inspection.

The man I had to fight has now returned to the group, but instead of looking inside the cell handed him, he pitches it at the black sky, smiling into the face of those who watch. The cell floats slowly, unevenly down, but as it reaches the earth it continues to sink at an uninterrupted rate.

A thick silence has settled on the expedition.

11:12

The moon is two thirds melted—silver slaver off a lipless mouth. As we descend toward the glow it brightens and expands like a poisoned eye. The plants, sensing some impending necromancy, are quivering and reaching tentatively for the light, their agitation causing the air around us to beat with a tumid warmth. We walk apart to lessen the heat.

It's as if the earth is tipping us into our own blaze.

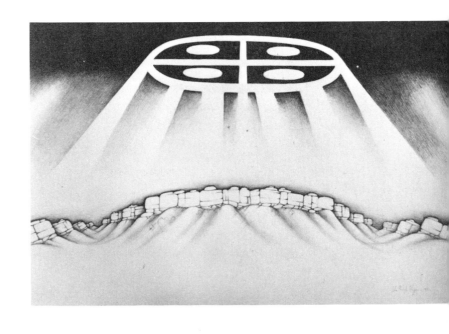

11:18

The glow has swollen to a monstrous booming radiance. We feel the whole white earth sucking down to its source. The plants, now large and tremulous, all arch toward the light, pulsing over us a crushing wave of heat. Only the suction of the rays saves us. We have long ago removed all clothing and I see the man's face clearly. I had not noticed it even when we fought.

11:20

We begin the climb down. The grade is almost vertical, but this is not a problem for me because the man and I have become inseparable. I now know I am the one without thought. He walks before me preparing the way, pulling each root and patting down the wrinkles. Frequently he looks back and smiles. Without warning I kick him and he plummets down the light. The expedition gathers in a circle and we listen to his lambent scream. Only the old woman is silent.

11:23

We have mastered a technique which has greatly simplified our descent. By jumping out and quickly extending our legs perpendicular to the light, while keeping them flexed tightly together, we have found that the force of the light will sustain the body gently downward and simultaneously warm the buttocks. The old woman will talk of nothing else. I had to remove her teeth so we could meditate on our flight.

11:25

As carefully as one might watch the intent behind the eyes of a man who approaches at night, we have been studying the form focusing below us, a shape wide and serrate shadowed beneath the light. It deepens as we descend. Its edges are tipped in a gauzy red. We are in the midst of a great speculation about it and everyone is an authority. The old woman entertains us by recalling parallel forms of the past, her eyes vivid with the telling. No one can understand her; nevertheless, we laugh heartily at every gummed punch line and she is pleased.

11:27

The form below the light is beginning to move, un-clenching like the jaw it resembles. We cannot look away. Our concentration attenuates the light, causing our fall to distend. The realization of what this prin-ciple could have done for us is a hammer beating at our temples.

The jaw is open.

11:31
___

Now that we see where we are headed, a great
body is taken from our spirit. We join hands in flight
and breathe the tip of our reality.

11:32

Behind me I hear the boy and the old woman.

It was so simple.
Yes, if we had only known.
But what would we have done?
Done?
If we had known—what would we have done?

No one knows; it's just that knowing is so much better.

Of course. And will we be together after?
Who can think of after?
Of course.

11:35

The light is imploding. The woman-without-shirt made the mistake of getting too far to the center and dropped like guano. We are unable to see her in the teeth.

11:37

The light is heavy with strangulation, compressed in a final lunar leak. The white moon mellows nothing, warms nothing, sinks. Our descent is frozen. The rays cut us like an uncontracted maw.

11:39

Behind me the poet has once again begun his infernal recitation. I will not waste even a glance. Inexplicably the light dilates and we fall free. No one will speak to him.

11:41

We are close enough now to see bodies broken over the teeth. The woman is impaled on top of the man, a crooked cross. Her fingers are clenched in violent unreaching. I will not look away.

11:42

The teeth are upon us. We hear a sere wind. Moans blowing by. Squirms falling to the ground. Is there nothing?

11:43

Fork of light in the nostrils, and an eye looks down at me. Flat like a ceiling light, soulless and flat, and with a flat polar stare. It hangs as still as a dead lip, letting all time burn down around it.

I am through the jaw.
The bats are waiting.

Of that time which moves and moves no more
I come to take white death and paint lament
long embered winter lines
and tread to dust the coming rage of spring
and snap the nursing vine (time's twin maiden
inside the turning of the line)
to shim against a fallen crystal sleeve
(fallen in deep red canterbury)

Of that time when babes suckle wit
and labor more into a glassy hole
(piece by piece and evermore)
I come to take apart the good upwinding plug
and see before me a lamb twice slaughtered
no coming or a coming gained
no greater than before
(and still that light pulses into black
there is no denying that)

Of that time I know not of, I shall begin
and wince into a muggy stomach
more than this I cannot
for who among them knows the ticking sweet
that leads to shadows once before

Hugh Prather
April 1974
Santa Fe,
New Mexico